GLASGOW G61 3SU
TEL: 0141-942 2297

INTRODUCTION ...

- These student worksheets are intended to act alongside the corresponding revision guide to help reinforce your understanding and improve your confidence.

- Every worksheet is cross-referenced to
  'The Essentials of G.C.S.E. Design and Technology: Food Technology' edited by Janet Inglis

- The questions concentrate purely on the content you need to cover, and the limited space forces you to choose your answer carefully.

These worksheets can be used ...

... as <u>classwork sheets</u> where pupils use their revision guide to provide the answers ...

... as <u>harder classwork sheets</u> where pupils study the topic first, then answer the questions without their guides ...

... as easy to mark <u>homework sheets</u> which test understanding and reinforce learning ...

... as the basis for <u>learning homeworks</u> which are then tested in subsequent lessons ...

... as <u>test material</u> for topics or entire modules ...

... as <u>a structured revision programme</u> prior to the exams.

- Remember to fill in your score at the bottom of each page in the small grey box ⬜ , and also to put your score in the 'marks' column on the contents page.

CONTRIBUTORS: Janet Inglis, Immanuel C.E. Community College, Bradford;
Judith Sunderland, Hanson Technology College, Bradford;
Christine Finch, Hanson Technology College, Bradford;
Angela Tooley, Hanson Technology College, Bradford.

CONTENTS

1. Complete, and give examples of, the names of each food group. Fill in the number of portions a day which should be eaten.

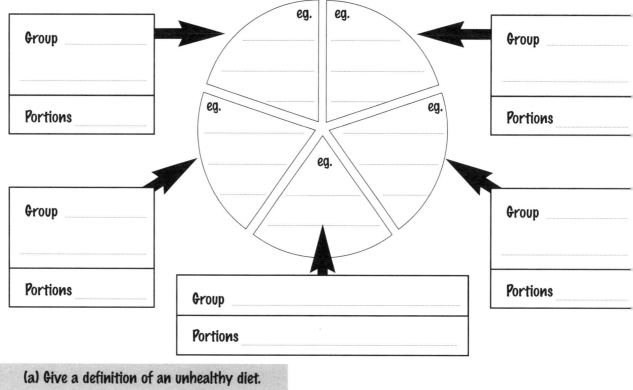

Group ....
....

Portions ....

eg. ....   eg. ....

Group ....
....

Portions ....

eg. ....

eg. ....

Group ....
....

Portions ....

eg. ....

Group ....
....

Portions ....

Group ....

Portions ....

2. (a) Give a definition of an unhealthy diet.

(b) List 6 different illnesses, which could be caused by a poor diet.

(i) ....

(ii) ....

(iii) ....

(iv) ....

(v) ....

(vi) ....

3. Study these labels. They are low in fat but are they healthy? Explain.

NUTRITION
(Typical Values per 100g): Energy Value 310 kJ (75 kcal), Protein 2 g MEDIUM, Carbohydrate 14 g HIGH (of which Sugars 11 g HIGH), Fat 0.8 g LOW (of which Saturates 0.5 g MEDIUM), Fibre 0.1 g LOW, Sodium Trace g LOW.

ALLERGY ADVICE
CONTAINS COWS MILK.
PRODUCED IN A FACTORY HANDLING NUTS.
THIS PRODUCT MAY CONTAIN CHERRY STONES.

NUTRITION INFORMATION		
Typical Values	Amount per 100g	Amount per Can
Energy	106kJ/25kcal	314kJ/74kcal
Protein	0.7g	2.0g
Carbohydrate (of which sugars)	4.6g (2.8g)	13.5g (8.1g)
Fat (of which saturates)	0.5g (Trace)	1.3g (0.1g)
Fibre	0.3g	0.9g
Sodium	0.3g	1.0g

Source of Vitamin C & Iron.
Low in Fat.

Nutrition Information Typical Values	per 100g	per 25g
Energy	1270kJ 299kcal	317kJ 74kcal
Protein	0.9g	0.2g
Carbohydrate	73.6g	18.4g
(of which sugars)	70.2g	17.8g
Fat	0.1g	<0.1g
(of which saturates)	<0.1g	<0.1g
Fibre	5.1g	1.3g
Sodium	0.3g	<0.1g
Vitamins		
Vitamin C	43mg (72% RDA)	11mg (18% RDA)
Minerals		
Iron	10mg (72% RDA)	2.5mg (18% RDA)

4.   (a) Why do manufacturers make 'Healthy Option' foods?

(b) What must a consumer be aware of when purchasing 'Healthy Option' foods?

(c) Explain what is meant by organic food.

(d) What is GM food?

5.   (a) Lucy is six years old, she takes a packed lunch to school every day. Lucy's mum wants to provide healthy meals for Lucy. Would you consider the following packed lunches to be healthy options? List the reasons for your answer.

(i)   Cheese sandwich in white bread, packet of crisps, can of diet fizzy lemon and an orange.

(ii)   Chocolate spread in wholemeal bread, orange squash and an apple.

(iii) Beef sandwich made with white bread, packet of crisps, can of diet cola and a small bag of grapes.

(b) Plan two suitable packed meals for Lucy. Give reasons for your choices.

1. (a) Name the main functions of protein in the body.

(b) (i) Proteins are made up of

(ii) These combine together to make

(c) There are _____ essential amino acids which the body cannot make and they
are found in protein from animal _____ and in _____ beans.
These foods are said to have a _____ .
Proteins found in other plant sources have a _____ .
This means that they lack some essential amino acids and these foods will need to be eaten together.

2. Sort out the following foods into animal and plant sources of protein.
Eggs, Fish, Soya beans, Rice, Yoghurt, Baked beans, Cereals, Milk, Bread, Meat, Cheese, Peas.

PLANT SOURCES	ANIMAL SOURCES

3. Which of the following contain the most protein?

(i) 100g of baked beans or 200g of egg

(ii) 150g of fish or 100g of beef

(iii) 100g of egg or 150g of potatoes

4. What are the sources of the following proteins?

(i) Casein

(ii) Albumin

(iii) Gluten

(iv) Collagen

(v) Lactalbumin

1.   (a) Write a definition for 'alternative proteins'.

_____

(b) Who might eat alternative proteins and why?

(i) _____

Why? _____

(ii) _____

Why? _____

(iii) _____

Why? _____

2.   (a) Fill in the table below to name 4 different alternative protein foods, and explain what they are made from.

(i)	(ii)
Made from	Made from
(iii)	(iv)
Made from	Made from

(b) List 12 advantages of using alternative proteins.

(i) _____

(ii) _____

(iii) _____

(iv) _____

(v) _____

(vi) _____

(vii) _____

(viii) _____

(ix) _____

(x) _____

(xi) _____

(xii) _____

1. Fats have different uses in the body. Fill in the chart below.

USES	EXPLANATION

2. Fats have different functions during the manufacture of food products. List these and give an example (other than the example in your guide) of a product which uses this function.

FUNCTION IN FOOD PRODUCTION	EXAMPLE

3. (a) Explain how a food manufacturer could make a product healthier.

(b) Explain what the benefits would be to the consumer.

(c) Give an example of a product which has been made healthier in this way.

1. Complete the following paragraph.

Carbohydrates are a very important part of our _____ . They are useful for providing _____ , and when working in conjunction with _____ , they help the body to _____ and _____ .

2. (a) Name 3 different types of carbohydrate.

(i) _____   (ii) _____   (iii) _____

(b) State what each type of carbohydrate is formed from.

(i) _____   (ii) _____   (iii) _____

(c) Give 2 examples of each type of carbohydrate.

(i) _____   (ii) _____   (iii) _____

3. (a) What might a food manufacturer use to sweeten food?

_____

(b) LACTOSE and FRUCTOSE are linked to sugar. How could you tell that just from looking at the words.

_____

4. (a) Name 2 different foods which you might eat if you needed some energy quickly to keep you going until lunchtime. Explain your choices.

_____

(b) Explain why someone taking part in a marathon might eat pasta before a race?

_____

(c) By looking at the foods which contain sugars and starches, can you explain why we, as a nation, are becoming obese?

_____

1. Complete the following paragraph.

Vitamins are compounds made up of _____ , _____ and _____ .
They have many different functions: they can help our bodies build and _____ , they
control the release of _____ and they can prevent illness. Many vitamins _____
be stored in the body, so we must eat them every _____ .

2. (a) Explain why you wouldn't necessarily become deficient in
Vitamin D if you didn't have some in your diet every day.

(b) What is Vitamin D also known as?

(c) Name 2 good sources of Vitamin D. (i) (ii)

(d) Why is Vitamin D important?

(e) Name 2 groups of people who need to ensure that they receive enough Vitamin D.

(i) (ii)

3. (a) List 4 animal sources of Vitamin A.

(i) (ii) (iii) (iv)

(b) Name (i) 2 fruits and (ii) 2 vegetables which contain carotene.

(i) (ii)

(c) Why do you think Vitamin A is added to margarine by law?

(d) Explain the effects of a deficiency in Vitamin A.

4. (a) Name 2 good sources of Vitamin E. (i) (ii)

(b) Explain the functions of Vitamin E

5.   (a) Name 7 good sources of Vitamin K.

(i) _____   (v) _____

(ii) _____   (vi) _____

(iii) _____   (vii) _____

(iv) _____

(b) Give 2 reasons why we need Vitamin K.

(i) _____

(ii) _____

6.   (a) Name the 4 main vitamins in the Vitamin B complex.

(i) _____   (iii) _____

(ii) _____   (iv) _____

(b) List 6 foods which are a good supply of the Vitamin B complex.

(i) _____   (iii) _____   (v) _____

(ii) _____   (iv) _____   (vi) _____

(c) Why must pregnant women ensure that they eat enough folic acid?

7.   (a) Explain the effects of a deficiency of Vitamin C in the diet.

(b) Vitamin C is also known as _____ . It _____ in water and is
easily destroyed by _____ . It helps absorb _____ and _____
from food and protects us against _____ and _____ .

(c) Name 3 foods which contain Vitamin C.

(i) _____   (ii) _____   (iii) _____

1. Complete the following chart.

MINERAL	SOURCES	FUNCTION	RESULT OF DEFICIENCY
CALCIUM			
POTASSIUM			
IRON			
PHOSPHORUS			
SODIUM			
IODINE			
FLUORIDE			

2.   (a) Which 2 minerals work together to help form healthy bones and teeth?

(b) A food manufacturer wishes to produce a product to be sold as part of a healthy option range. Which mineral could they reduce and why might they choose to do so?

3.   Tick the minerals found in the different foods.

FOOD	CALCIUM	POTASSIUM	IRON	PHOSPHORUS	SODIUM	IODINE	FLUORIDE
Liver							
Meat							
Sardines							
Dried Fruit							
Yeast Extract							
Milk							
Cocoa							
Pulses							
Bananas							
Cheese							
Eggs							
Wholemeal Bread							
White Bread							
Green Vegetables							
Seafood							
Some Water							

1. Name three sources from which starch can be obtained for use during food production.

(i) _____

(ii) _____

(iii) _____

2. Explain in your own words, the six stages involved in the process of gelatinisation.

3. (a) Explain how you can avoid a lumpy sauce.

(b) Explain two ways in which the thickness of a sauce can be altered.

4. (a) Food manufacturers often use SMART STARCHES.
Give a definition of a smart starch, in your own words.

(b) Explain why a manufacturer might use a smart starch for each of the following products.

A weight watcher's salad cream ➡ _____

Low calorie biscuits ➡ _____

A packet of instant custard ➡ _____

Fish in parsley sauce (frozen) ➡ _____

1. (a) Name the three main sources of fats and oils.

(i) _____   (ii) _____   (iii) _____

(b) Give three examples of each source (try to think of at least one example for each source which isn't in your revision guide).

(i)

(ii)

(iii)

2. Explain the main difference between fats and oils.

3. Put the following food products into the correct columns in the chart.

Sunflower oil Dripping	FATS-	OILS-
Soft margarine Lard		
Suet Block margarine		
Rape-seed oil Low fat spread		
Fish oils Cream		
Olive oil Sesame oil		

4. Explain why food manufacturers produce items using low fat or reduced fat products.

5. Explain why fats might be used for the following.

On top of pâté	
In sandwiches	
In chocolate cake	
In bread	
Served over vegetables	
In jam tart pastry	

1.   **(a) Where is sugar obtained from?**

(b) List 10 different types of sugar which can be used in food processing.

(i) _____   (iii) _____   (v) _____   (vii) _____   (ix) _____

(ii) _____   (iv) _____   (vi) _____   (viii) _____   (x) _____

2.   Complete the chart below to show the functions of sugar in different dishes.

PRODUCT CONTAINING SUGAR	FUNCTION
Strawberry jam	
Ice cream	
Red wine	
A Victoria sandwich cake	
Apple puree	
Baked beans	
A sliced loaf of bread	

3.   **(a) Write a definition of dextrinisation.**

(b) Write a definition of caramelisation.

4.   **(a) Explain why there has been an increase in the amount of artificial sweeteners used by the food industry.**

(b) Circle the artificial sweeteners used in these two products.

INGREDIENTS

Tomatoes (59%), Water
Modified Cornflour, Sugar
Salt, Dried Skimmed Milk
Vegetable Oil, Whey Protein
Acesulfame Potassium
Spice Extracts, Herb Extract

SPARKLING CHERRY FLAVOUR
SOFT DRINK WITH
SUGAR AND SWEETNERS
INGREDIENTS
Carbonated Water, Sugar,
Citric Acid, Flavouring, Aspartame,
Acesulfame K, Preservative (Sodium
Benzoate), Colour (Carmoisine).

1. List four different birds which produce eggs normally eaten in Britain.

(i) .... (ii) .... (iii) .... (iv) ....

2. What do these sentences describe?

(i) The action of whisking egg whites to incorporate air bubbles in the mixture. ....

(ii) Heating eggs until they solidify. ....

(iii) Using egg yolk to hold oil and water together in a suspension. ....

3. (a) Complete the following paragraphs.

(i) When an egg white is whisked the .... is stretched and this incorporates .... These are then .... down into smaller bubbles, which are surrounded by a .... of .... This is called a .... It remains stable because the .... generated by .... partially .... it.

(ii) An .... is formed when .... and water are forcibly combined. However, an .... must be used if the oil and water are to remain in this .... One example of an emulsifier is .... which is found in egg ....

(b) At what temperature do . . .

(i) Egg whites coagulate? .... (ii) Egg yolks coagulate? ....

4. (a) Why is it advisable to cook eggs?

(b) Who should avoid eating raw egg?

(c) How do food manufacturers reduce the risk of food poisoning from egg in their products?

1. Explain what is meant by OFFAL.

2. Put the following into the correct columns:
Pork, kidney, lamb, chicken, turkey, rabbit, brains, liver, venison, tripe, goose, quail.

TYPE OF MEAT	TYPE OF POULTRY	TYPE OF OFFAL

3. (a) Explain the difference between the cooking methods of meat with short muscle fibres and meat with large muscle fibres.

(b) Why are meats tenderised?

4. (a) Why does meat become easier to digest when it is cooked?

(b) What happens if meat is overcooked?

5. (a) Why was there a decline in the demand for beef products in the 1990s?

(b) (i) Which religious group(s) do not eat pork?

(ii) Which religious group(s) do not eat beef?

(c) What is 'Kosher' or 'Halal' meat?

1. Put the following into the correct columns:
Crabs, oysters, herring, cod, plaice, shrimps, coley, mackerel, lobster, sole, trout, haddock, mussels, whiting, prawns, sardine, scallops, cockles, turbot.

WHITE FISH		SHELLFISH		OILY FISH
ROUND	FLAT	CRUSTACEANS	MOLLUSCS	

2. (a) Why must great care be taken when storing or preparing fish?

(b) How is it possible for caught fish to remain in peak condition until they reach a processing plant?

3. Most fish is taken to factories where it may be preserved. Complete the following chart.

PRESERVATION	TYPES OF FISH USED
Smoking	
Canning	
Freezing	

4. Fishcakes and fish fingers are two examples of secondary processing of fish. List 3 others.

(i)   (ii)   (iii)

5. (a) Explain in your own words, why the flesh of fish is always tender.

(b) At what temperature does the flesh of fish start to denature?

6. Explain fully how fish stocks can be preserved to ensure that there is always a supply of fish.

1. Complete the following crossword.

ACROSS

2. A nutrient of milk which aids growth and repair.
3. A mineral which is found in milk.
5. A milk whose flavour is altered by processing.
8. A nutrient found in milk which helps release energy from food.
10. A very creamy milk with more fat than other types.
13. The cream is evenly spread throughout this milk.
14. A nutrient found in milk which helps bones to grow and aids night vision.
15. Water has been removed from this type of milk.
16. A nutrient needed to keep bones and teeth strong.

DOWN

1. A thick and sweet milk.
2. Heated to $72°C$ for 15 seconds, then cooled rapidly
4. This is often removed or reduced to provide healthy option milk.
6. This milk is sterilized at $115-120°C$ for 10 minutes.
7. Provides the sweetness of milk.
9. Also known as 'long life' milk.
11. This has had some of the cream removed.
12. All of the fat has been removed.

2. Explain what is meant by HOMOGENIZATION.

3. When manufacturers are deciding which milk to use what should they consider and why?

(i)

(ii)

(iii)

(iv)

(v)

(vi)

1. List the standard components which can be produced by the secondary processing of milk and give 3 different examples of each.

Standard Component	Example 1	Example 2	Example 3

2. Complete the chart below.

Type of Cream	Examples of use
Single	
Double	
Whipping	
Aerosol	
Crème Fraîche	
Clotted	
Sour	

3. (a) Represent graphically the amount of protein, water and fat found in cheddar cheese.

(b) Which vitamins does cheese contain?

(c) Explain why low temperatures and short cooking times are best when manufacturing products containing cheese.

4. How could you reduce the fat content of dishes containing dairy foods?

1. A food technician is making prototype loaves in a test kitchen. List the ingredients required for one loaf.

Bread - basic recipe	In addition to the recipe, what other information would be needed before the bread could be made?

2. When the bread was cooked the following problems had occurred.
Explain what might have happened and what action would need to be taken in the future.

FAULT		REASON	FUTURE ACTION
Bread insufficiently risen	(i)		
	(ii)		
Very close crumb texture			
Burnt			
Unevenly risen			
Salty flavour			

3. Explain the three following terms.

(i) GLUTEN -

(ii) DEXTRINISATION -

(iii) CARAMELISATION -

4. What differences would there be ...

(i) If wholemeal flour was used instead of strong plain flour in the making of bread?

(ii) If dried fruit was added to the dough in the making of bread?

(iii) If cheese was added to the surface in the making of bread?

1. Which pastry could be used in the following products?

PRODUCT	TYPE OF PASTRY
Apple turnovers	
Apple dumplings	
Fruit flans	
Chocolate eclairs	

2. (a) Explain what is meant by the term 'shorten' in pastry making.

(b) Complete the following table to show the function of each ingredient in pastry.

INGREDIENT	FUNCTION	INGREDIENT	FUNCTION
Flour		Water	
Fat		Salt	

3. A food manufacturer wishes to make a healthier option shortcrust pastry. He wishes to modify the following recipe: 100g plain flour, 25g butter, 25g lard, 0.5g salt, 20ml cold water.

(a) Give 3 reasons why the manufacturer might want to do this.

(i)

(ii)

(iii)

(b) (i) How could the amount of NSP (fibre) in the recipe be increased?

(ii) What effect would this modification have on the recipe?

(c) (i) Explain how the amount of saturated fat could be reduced in the basic recipe.

(ii) What effect would this have on the final product?

1. (a) State what the following ratios would be in cake making.

(i) flour to margarine in a creamed mixture

(ii) flour to egg in a whisked mixture

(b) What differences are there in the ingredients needed for creamed cakes and whisked cakes?

2. Explain the following during cake manufacture.

(a) Sugar gives texture

(b) Sugar gives colour

(c) Flour adds structure

(d) Eggs help to form the framework

(e) Margarine lightens the texture

3. Explain why a commercially produced swiss roll has a longer shelf-life than a homemade swiss roll.

4. Explain what is meant by aeration and give 3 ways in which this can be achieved in cake making.

5.. Explain, using labels and diagrams, how you could add a decorative finish to the cakes below.

A plain whisked sponge cake	A creamed chocolate cake
Plan view Side view	

1. Three types of sauce can be made by the Roux method. Complete the chart below and suggest a product on which each sauce can be used.

TYPE OF SAUCE	INGREDIENTS	EXAMPLE OF USE OF SAUCE
Coating		

2. (a) Use a diagram and words to explain how you could test the thickness of a sauce.

(b) What would you expect to see if you tested equal amounts of a panada, coating and pouring sauce?

3. Explain how flour, cornflour and arrowroot thicken a sauce.

4. Give detailed reasons why a sauce might contain lumps.

5. What modifications could you make to your sauce in order to...

(i) add flavour?

(ii) reduce the fat content?

1. Before you can amend the ingredients in any dish you must first understand their function. Ingredients must be replaced by other ingredients which have the same function.
For example, stock is used as the liquid in a casserole but could be replaced by beer, wine, orange juice or tomato juice. This would change the flavour of the product. Complete the charts below giving the function of each ingredient and an alternative product which could be used.

(i) Bread Rolls

INGREDIENT	FUNCTION	ALTERNATIVE
Strong plain flour		
Yeast		
Water		
Salt		
Poppy seeds		

(ii) Beef Casserole

INGREDIENT	FUNCTION	ALTERNATIVE
Stewing steak		
Red wine		
Bay leaf		
Onion		
Flour		
Carrots		
Sweetcorn		
Red pepper		

2. Combination dishes are made up of separate secondary processed products eg. lasagne is made from meat sauce, pasta and cheese sauce. Identify the separate parts of the following combination dishes.

(i) Fish Pies

(ii) Cornish Pasty

(iii) Trifle

(iv) Moussaka

(v) Samosa

(vi) Lemon Meringue Pie

(vii) Egg and Bacon Flan

1. Complete the paragraph below.

Food ages and _____ over time. These changes occur more quickly in _____ foods. Foods which are processed will last for a _____ period of time. The changes which take place are caused by _____ and _____ . Some changes are beneficial, other changes are _____ .

2. Draw lines to correctly match the following.

If enzyme activity is allowed to continue ...	... fruit to ripen, meat to tenderise and oxidisation to speed up.
Enzymes are ...	... all cells.
Enzymes break down ...	... food spoilage occurs.
Enzymes cause ...	... plant and animal tissues.
Enzymes are found in ...	... chemical catalysts.

3. (a) What is oxidation also known as?

(b) Explain fully, in your own words, how oxidation occurs.

(c) Fully explain all the different methods by which oxidation can be prevented.

1. (a) Describe the microorganisms which are found naturally on the skins of fruit and in the air.

(b) What are moulds?

2. Explain how the following are used in the food industry.

MOULDS

YEASTS

BACTERIA

3. Complete the following table.

BACTERIA	SOURCE
Listeria Monocytogenes	
	Found in raw meat.
Salmonella	
	Found in cooked rice, lentils and beans.
Staphylococcus Aureus	

4. List the symptoms you would expect to see in cases of food poisoning.

(i)   (iv)

(ii)   (v)

(iii)

5. Which groups of people are at particular risk from food poisoning?

6. (a) What is meant by cross-contamination?

(b) Explain how cross-contamination can be avoided in the food industry and at home.

1.   (a) Why do food producers need to control the growth of bacteria?

(b) What do we need to know if we want to stop the growth of bacteria?

2.   Complete the table below to show the conditions needed for bacterial growth, how to control their growth and relevant examples of food. The first one has been done for you.

BACTERIA NEED	GROWTH IS CONTROLLED BY	EXAMPLES OF FOOD
Time	Eating quickly or chilling rapidly after cooking.	Cook-chill products

3.   Draw lines to correctly match the following.

Freezing or chilling ...	... moisture is not available for microorganisms.
Drying food removes ...	... in packaging for other gases.
Freezing turns liquids to solids and therefore ...	... slows down the rate of bacterial reproduction.
Systems are available which exchange the air ...	... heated to above 62°C to reduce bacterial growth.
Food should be cooled to below 5°C or ...	... the water, preventing bacterial growth.

4.   Explain what is meant by the following.

(i) M.A.P.

(ii) C.A.P.

1. What does this symbol mean?

---

2. Complete the following sentences, using the words below.

active, dormant, 121, warm, reproducing, atmospheric, gas, low, preservatives, oxygen, bacteria, reproduce, slowed, packaging, grow, high, growth, reproduction, spores, prevent, defrosting

All _____ and _____ can be destroyed by _____ temperatures ie. above _____ °C.

Chemical _____ may also destroy bacteria or _____ them _____ .

Alternatively, as most bacteria need _____ to grow and reproduce, the _____ in the packaging can be altered, thus preventing _____ and _____ . This is known as M.A.P. or Modified _____ . The growth and reproduction of bacteria can also be _____ down by _____ temperatures until the bacteria are _____ ie. they are not able to _____ and _____ . The bacteria will become _____ when the food becomes _____ due to _____ .

---

3. Complete the following table. Use the examples below as well as trying to include some examples of your own.

METHOD OF PRESERVATION	EXAMPLES OF FOOD

Dried potato	Frozen pizza	Fresh coffee	Instant coffee
Jam	Pasteurised milk	Dried fruit	Pasteurised fruit juices
Fresh meat	Baked beans	Sterilised milk	Dried peas
Bacon	Fresh vegetables	Smoked fish	Frozen chips

1. Mark the following information on the temperature scale below.
Devise a suitable system to show your answers

(i) The freezing point of water.
(ii) The boiling point of water.
(iii) The temperature range at which cook-chill dishes should be chilled after first cooking.
(iv) The temperature range for storing chilled foods.
(v) The temperature range for storing frozen foods.
(vi) The minimum temperature to which cook-chill dishes should be reheated.

-40°C	-20°C	0°C	20°C	40°C	60°C	80°C	100°C	120°C	

2. Explain the difference between cook-chill food and chilled food.

3. Put the following foods into the correct columns.

Ham, prawn cocktail, moussaka, cream cheese, scotch egg, lamb casserole, pork pie, vegetable curry, egg sandwich, shepherds pie, cheese, stir fried beef, chicken korma, potato-topped fish pie, lasagne, quiche lorraine.

COOK-CHILL PRODUCTS	CHILLED FOOD PRODUCTS

4. Why is there now a high demand for frozen food?

5. (a) Explain the process of accelerated freeze drying (AFD)

(b) What advantages are there in producing food products using this process?

1.   (a) Explain what is meant by the term 'shelf-life'.

(b) Why do manufacturers need to extend the shelf-life of products?

2.   (a) Complete the following table.

METHOD OF PRESERVATION	HOW IT WORKS	ADVANTAGE AND DISADVANTAGE
Pasteurisation		
Sterilisation		
UHT		
Irradiation		
Canning		

(b) A food manufacturer wants to extend the shelf-life of the following food products.
    What method of preservation would you recommend in each case? (Explain your choice)

(i) Blackberries

(ii) Milk

(iii) Carton of soup

(iv) Sweetcorn

(v) Baby food

1.   (a) Explain what the prefix 'E' stands for in additives.

(b) Why is the 'E' number used in place of the chemical name of the additive?

2.   Complete the following table.

ADDITIVES	USE	FOOD PRODUCTS WHICH CONTAIN THESE ADDITIVES
E100s		
E200s		
E300s		
E400s		

3.   Apart from the additives in the table above, name four other additives which are commonly used in the food industry.

(i)   (ii)

(iii)   (iv)

4.   (a) Why is it important that all food products have labels that list the additives they contain?

(b) Give one advantage of using additives in food products.

1. What is the difference between CAD and CAM?

2. Explain fully how you can use computers in your Food Technology course.

3. (a) In your own words, explain the advantages of using computers for designing products in the food industry

(b) Using computers can also have its disadvantages. List as many as you can think of.

4. Explain how CAD is used in the food industry.

5. (a) What is primary research?

(b) Explain what spreadsheets are and how they work.

1. A student carried out a questionnaire about snacks.
The results of three different questions are shown below.

Q. How old are you?

Age (years)	12	13	14	15	16
Number of people	2	5	9	3	1

Q. Which of the following do you eat regularly?

Type of Snack	Pizza	Fruit	Sausage Roll	Samosa	Sandwich	Kebab	Crisps	Burger	Chocolate
Regularly eaten	20	6	2	8	20	5	20	16	15
Not Regularly eaten	0	14	18	12	0	15	0	4	5

Q. Which of the following do you consider to be the most important factor about a snack?

Type of Snack	Number of people
Snack should be hot	3
Snack can be eaten with hands	11
Snack is low cost	4
Snack is trendy	2

Use different types of graph to present each set of results in the space below.

2. The specification of a new snack stated that the product should have a crisp, crunchy and dry pastry with a spicy, meaty and moist filling. The sensory testing was carried out by a team of trained testers. The results are shown below.

Tester 1
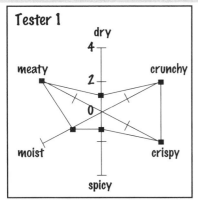

Tester 2
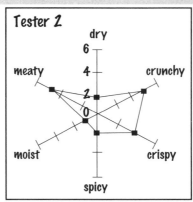

Tester 3
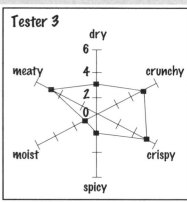

Using the information from the testers, identify **3** characteristics which should be improved and suggest **2** improvements for each.

(i)

(ii)

(iii)

3. A manufacturer wishes to develop a new pasta product which is high in NSP (dietary fibre) and low in fat. Below is the nutritional analysis for a standard lasagne recipe.

g	FOOD	g Protein	g Fat	g CHO	g Sugar	g Starch	g Fibre	kCal	KJ	mg Na	mg Ca	mg Fe	µg VitA	µg VitD	mg VitC	mg VitE
175	Lasagne (boil)	5.3	1.1	39	1	38	2.5	175	742	2	11	1	0.0	0.0	0.0	0.0
375	Whole Milk	12	15	18	18	0.0	0.0	248	1031	206	431	0.0	274	0.0	4	0.0
25	Margarine	0.0	20	0.0	0.0	0.0	0.0	185	760	200	1	0.0	383	2	0.0	2.0
25	Plain White Flour	2.5	0.3	20	0.0	20	0.9	88	373	1	38	1	0.0	0.0	0.0	0.0
2	Mustard Powder	1	1	0.0	0.0	0.0	0.0	9	38	0.0	7	0.2	0.0	0.0	0.0	0.0
100	Cheddar Cheese	26	34	0.0	0.0	0.0	0.0	412	1708	670	720	0.0	550	0.0	0	0.5
200	Raw Beef Mince	37.6	32.4	0.0	0.0	0.0	0.0	442	1824	172	30.0	5	0.0	0.0	0	0.2
400	Canned Tomatoes	4.0	0.4	12.0	11	1	3.2	64	276	156	48.0	2	880	0.0	48	4.9
100	Tomato Puree	5	0.0	13	13	0.3	2.8	68	357	240	48	1.6	1300	0.0	38.0	5.4
2	Oregano	0.0	0.0	1	0.0	0.0	0.0	6	26	0.0	32	0.9	83	0.0	0.0	0.0

(a) What is the total amount of fibre in this product?

(b) List the 4 ingredients which contain the greatest amount of fat.

(i)   (ii)

(iii)   (iv)

(c) Give **3** ways of increasing the fibre content.

(i)   (ii)

(iii)

(d) Give **3** ways of reducing the fat content.

(i)   (ii)

(iii)

1. Below are the answers to some questions about the use of digital cameras. Can you work out what the questions were.

(i) To ensure that the manufacturer knows how the finished dish should look.

(ii) Photographs show the changes that occur when recipes are modified.

(iii) They can be used in flow charts to show how to make a product.

(iv) They show evidence of products you have made for the Long Task.

2. (a) Explain how data logging may be used in the manufacturing of the following products.

(i) Yoghurt:

(ii) Bread:

(iii) Cook-chill dishes:

(b) Data logging can be used as part of the designing process or in manufacturing. State 3 ways in which it is used in designing.

(i)

(ii)

(iii)

1. Why do food manufacturers find computers more useful than humans in many stages of production?

2. (a) A manufacturer of treacle sponge puddings wishes to introduce five new control processes into the manufacturing system. In the space below draw a table to illustrate the name of each control process, the general use of each one and how each will be used specifically within his factory

(b) Explain fully how the above changes might affect the current jobs of workers within the factory.

1. **(a)** When drawing a production line, there are some standard diagrams which can be used. These might be either two-dimensional or three-dimensional. Name the diagrams shown below.

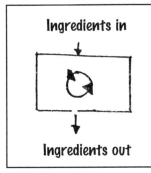

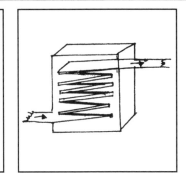

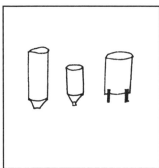

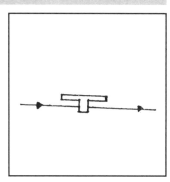

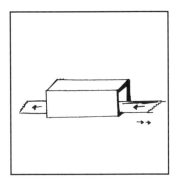

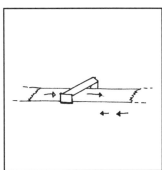

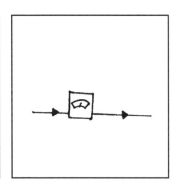

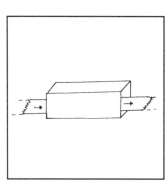

(b) In the boxes below draw the named diagrams in either two- or three-dimensions.

Enrober	Wrapper	Freezer Tunnel	Mixer which moves on floor

2. In the space below, sketch a production line to illustrate how jam tarts can be made on a large scale in industry.

1. (a) Below are the 16 stages in the design process for the development of food products. Put them in the correct order. The first one has been done for you.

A. Product Formulation	B. Selection and Modification	C. Future Development	D. Concept Screening
E. Final Manufacturing Specification	F. First Production Run	G. Design Brief and Design Specification	H. Consumer Testing
I. Test Marketing	J. Market Research	K. Commercial Viability	L. Generation of Ideas
M. Sensory Evaluation	N. Modifications	O. Initial Brief	P. Product Launch

0 → □ → □ → □ → □ → □ → □ → □

□ ← □ ← □ ← □ ← □ ← □ ← □ ← □

(b) Write an explanation of each stage. The first one has been done for you.

STAGE	EXPLANATION
1. Initial Brief	Set by the manufacturer and issued to the Development Team
2.	
3.	
4.	
5.	
6.	
7.	
8.	
9.	
10.	
11.	
12.	
13.	
14.	
15.	
16.	

1. (a) Why is presentation so important?

(b) Explain why planning your work is so important

2. (a) Explain the importance of the following with regards to your coursework.

(i) Number of pages used:

(ii) A margin on your work:

(iii) A photocopier:

(iv) A ruler during mounting work:

(v) Images:

(b) What type of bindings should NOT be used and why?

(c) Name 2 things which might be helpful in the presentation of your work if it is handwritten.

(i)   (ii)

3. (a) Explain how you would illustrate the differences between 2 similar dishes, eg. 2 cakes.

(b) A class of children were asked what their favourite type of pizza is.
Present the data in a graph format of your choice.

TYPE OF PIZZA	NO. OF CHILDREN
Hawaiian	11
Pepperoni	8
Vegetarian	3
Four Seasons	3
Margherita	5

1.   What 3 things are proposals based on?

(i) ....   (ii) ....

(iii) ....

2.   What 5 things could your proposal include?

(i) ....   (ii) ....

(iii) ....   (iv) ....

(v) ....

3.   Below are two different dishes which are part of the proposals for a new product. Annotate the picture and complete the boxes for each product.

(a) Pizza

DESCRIPTION

MODIFICATIONS		
INGREDIENT	MODIFICATION	EFFECT

(b) Stuffed Jacket Potato

DESCRIPTION

MODIFICATIONS		
INGREDIENT	MODIFICATION	EFFECT

1. (a) Explain in your own words what is meant by Primary Research.

> _(blank answer box)_

(b) Explain in your own words what is meant by Secondary Research.

> _(blank answer box)_

2. How would you research the following?
Give a full explanation as to why you have chosen each type of research.

(a) What teenagers eat at lunchtime.

> _(blank answer box)_

(b) How much people would spend on a ready-made meal for one.

> _(blank answer box)_

(c) What a leading food manufacturer produces in their dessert range.

> _(blank answer box)_

3. In the box provided, present the information below in a suitable visual format.

Favourite Chocolate Bars
Chocolate-coated mega fingers   8
Double chocolate chunks   7
Chocolate waves   2
Chocolate crisps   5

> _(blank answer box)_

4. Using the following information, research what additives are found in soft drinks. What conclusions can you make?

Real Tropical Juice Drink - Ingredients
Water, Fruit Juices and Puree from concentrate (35%) (Orange juice, Pineapple juice, Apricot puree, Passionfruit juice, Apple juice, Lemon juice, Lime juice, Guava puree, Banana puree, Mango puree), Sugar, Citric acid, Flavourings, Colour (Beta carotene), Antioxidant (Ascorbic acid)

Coca Cola - Ingredients
Carbonated Water, Sugar, Colour (Caramel E 150d), Phosphoric Acid, Flavourings, Caffeine

Dilute Orange Juice - Ingredients
Water, Oranges, Glucose-Fructose Syrup, Sugar, Citric Acid, Acidity Regulator (Trisodium Citrate) Preservatives (Potassium Sorbate, Sodium Metabisulphate), Sweeteners (Aspartame, Saccharin), Flavourings, Stabiliser (E466), Vitamins (Niacin, Pantothenic Acid, B6, D, B12), Colour (Beta-Carotene). Contains a source of Phenylalanine.

Ribena - Ingredients
Water, Glucose Fructose Syrup, Blackcurrant juice (6%), Sucrose, Citric Acid, Vitamin C

Cherry Pop - Ingredients
Carbonated water, Sugar, Citric Acid, Flavouring, Sweeteners (Aspartame, Acesulfame K), Preservative (Sodium benzoate), Colour (Carmoisine)

5. You are to develop a savoury dish for a lacto-vegetarian. Use the internet to carry out some research. Explain what you found out and how you could use this information.

6. If you were a food producer, suggest how you could use a competitor's produce in your research.

7. Decide on three pieces of information you could request from a frozen food manufacturer which could help in researching a brief to produce a frozen sweet product. Make a list of points you would ask them.

1. (a) Explain what a design specification is.

(b) Explain what a product specification is.

(c) Explain what a manufacturing specification is.

2. Explain why you think design specifications are important

3. Explain the difference between essential criteria and desirable criteria.

4. Complete the table to show which of these points would be included in a Design Specification.

✓✗	POINT	✓✗	POINT
	Retail price		Nutritional analysis
	Scale of production (one-off, batch or mass)		Weight of product
	Approximate selling price		Portion size
	Target audience		Weight of ingredients
	Preservation method		Money off coupons
	Number of portions in product (eg. to serve one or to serve four)		Product name

5. Write a design specification for a luxury dessert which would be sold in a supermarket.

1. What is the difference between a Product Specification and a Design Specification?

2. Write a product specification for each of the following products.

(i) Breakfast snack-bar eg. Alpen/Fruit & Fibre

(ii) Layered supermarket salad

(iii) Wrap type sandwich

(iv) Low fat pudding eg. Weight Watchers chocolate mousse

3. This recipe will serve six. The cost of the ingredients are shown below. Work out the cost of production and the cost per portion.

Flour	225g	21p
Lard	50g	2p
Butter	50g	13p
Brown Sugar	50g	8p
Cooking Apples	675g	£1.14

THE PRACTICAL SESSION

1. (a) Using the diagram to help you write down, in your own words, the important hygiene factors which should be taken into consideration when preparing for a practical session.

(b) Before you begin a practical session what should you do if you have a cut on your hand? Explain why.

2. What is Hazard Analysis, Critical Control Point usually abbreviated to?

3. Which foods would you prepare on these chopping boards?

WHITE	RED	BLUE	GREEN	YELLOW	BROWN

4. On the spider diagram illustrate the practices which should always be followed when working with food.

DURING THE PRACTICAL

1. Fill in the missing spaces using the words below to help you.

equipment, terms, sheets, recipe, flow, specification, output, recording, read, process, ingredients, chart, available

(i) Before beginning any practical investigations you should _____ the _____ .

(ii) Write a product or manufacturing _____ so that you know what _____ will be required.

(iii) Make sure you understand all the _____ used in the recipe.

(iv) Write down the _____ . This could be done as a _____ .

(v) Be clear about what the _____ should look like.

(vi) Check what specialist _____ you will need and make sure that it is _____ .

(vii) Produce all the _____ ready to record your findings.

2. List six ways in which you could modify the recipe to carry out an investigation for your Long Task.

Apple Glazed Pork with Spaghetti

Serves 4

Ingredients:
1 — 11.5oz Can Apple Puree
3/4 — Cup Chicken Stock
2 — Tablespoons Soy Sauce
1/2 — Teaspoon Lemon Juice
1/2 — Teaspoon Sesame Oil
2 — Tablespoons Cornflour
1/8 — Teaspoon Ground Cinnamon
1lb — Pork Tenderloin Cut into 3/4" Cubes
1/4 — Cup All-purpose Flour
1 — Tablespoon Vegetable Oil
9oz — Spaghetti cooked according to instructions

Directions:
COMBINE puree, stock, soy sauce, lemon juice, sesame oil, cornflour and cinnamon in a small bowl; mix until smooth.
COAT pork with flour. Cook in vegetable oil until browned on all sides. Remove from pan. Add apple mixture to pan, stirring to loosen browned bits. Bring to boil. Reduce heat to low; add pork and cook, covered, for 10 minutes or until pork is thoroughly cooked and sauce is thickened. Serve over hot spaghetti.

1 _____
2 _____
3 _____
4 _____
5 _____
6 _____

3. Why is it important to change only one thing for each investigation?

4. (a) Edward has decided to investigate the way coleslaw could be made. Suggest three ways in which it could be prepared.

(i) _____
(ii) _____
(iii) _____

(b) How would these different methods affect the coleslaw?

(i) _____
(ii) _____
(iii) _____

5. Sabiha is making an apple pie using the recipe below. How could she alter the basic recipe? Suggest how the modifications would alter the taste, texture, appearance or nutritional value of the apple pie.

100g white plain flour
25g margarine
25g lard
500g cooking apples
50g granulated sugar

6. (a) Emma is a vegetarian. Suggest 3 ways in which she could change this recipe for Shepherd's Pie.

SHEPHERD'S PIE
200g minced beef
1 onion
salt & pepper
1 beef stock cube
200g potatoes
50g cheddar cheese

(i)
(ii)
(iii)

(b) Explain how the modifications would alter the taste, texture, appearance or nutritional value of the dish.

(c) How would she record the results of her investigation?

(d) Why is it important that she records all the results of her investigation?

1. A local bakery wants to extend the number of products it produces. Below is a recipe for a basic loaf of bread. Suggest two possible modifications and explain how each modification would affect the final product.

Bread
300g strong plain flour
2g salt
15g yeast
20g vegetable fat
220ml warm water

2. (a) The bakery also wants to improve its existing products. Below is their current chocolate cake recipe. Suggest three investigations they could carry out to develop this product.

Chocolate Cake
100g margarine
100g caster sugar
100g egg
100g SR flour

(b) Explain how the bakery can ensure these investigations result in a fair test.

(c) Describe how they can evaluate the new product.

1. Name each of the five senses and give 2 examples of foods which alert these senses (use different examples to those in your Revision Guide).

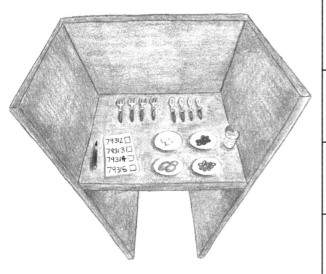

SENSE	FOOD

2. In industry food technologists often carry out sensory analysis. Fill in the rules they should follow and explain why each is important.

(i) Rule:

Why?

(ii) Rule:

Why?

(iii) Rule:

Why?

(iv) Rule:

Why?

(v) Rule:

Why?

(vi) Rule:

Why?

(vii) Rule:

Why?

1. Explain why sensory analysis is used.

2. (a) Explain what preference testing is.

(b) (i) What is a hedonic rating test?

(ii) Why is an uneven numbered scale used in this test?

(iii) What is a paired preference test?

(iv) Why are foods given numbers rather than names in these tests?

3. (a) If a manufacturer gave a tester 3 samples of a food, 2 of which were the same and asked them which was the odd one out, what sort of testing would they be carrying out?

(b) Explain what an A not A test is.

4. Draw a star profile for 2 products of your choice, making sure each product has at least 5 attributes

1. Write a definition of disassembly.

2. Disassemble the following products by annotating the photographs.

CAKE BARS

LASAGNE

3. Write a disassembly for a cheese sandwich.

1. Produce a manufacturing specification for a bread-based pizza . You have been given the ingredients for the base but you must decide on the toppings. Fill in the relevant information on the charts below.

MANUFACTURING SPECIFICATION			SCALING UP		
INPUT	SUPPLIER	COST	x10	x100	x1000
500g strong plain flour					
10g salt					
1 sachet dried yeast					
250ml water (37°C)					

Portion control

Costings

Total Cost

Other manufacturing costs would include

2. Portion Control is used to show how a manufacturer will ensure the portions are always the same during the manufacturing process. How would you suggest they carry out portion control on the following products? (Use annotated drawings to answer the question.)

(i) A single serving of spaghetti bolognaise.

(ii) A cook-chilled soup to be served in a carton.

(iii) Chocolate coated biscuits.

(iv) A single serving of a chilled strawberry dessert with a cream topping.

(v) Cheese and onion pasties

(vi) Sausage rolls

1. Explain why manufacturing specifications are necessary in the food industry.

2. (a) Complete the table to show which points would be included in a manufacturing specification for the following components. One has been done for you.

COMPONENT	POINTS TO INCLUDE
Eggs	Size, battery or free range, supplier, cost
Sugar	
Flour	
Milk	
Jam	
Tomatoes	
Yoghurt	

(b) Produce a table to show how you would alter the following recipe to produce a manufacturing specification for your coursework.

1kg mince beef
1 tin tomatoes
1 stock cube
1 tbsp tomato puree
pinch dried herbs
50ml semi-skimmed milk
2tbsp flour
50g margarine
salt & pepper
100g grated cheese

3. Annotated diagrams are used to show how the finished product should look. Draw and annotate a diagram for the following dishes.

Bread rolls	Chocolate cake

Layered salad	Samosas

4. The way in which products are divided into equal portions is usually included in the manufacturing specification. How would you ensure that the portions of these products were equal in size?

(i) Biscuits

(ii) Packets of crisps

(iii) Sausage rolls

(iv) Individual portions of fish pie

(v) Individual portions of a cake

1. Complete the following passage using the words below to help you.

simplifies, manufacturing, food, standard, reduce, standard

Commercial companies produce _____ components which are used in the
_____ industry. They are used to _____
the stages in manufacture which _____ production. They can also be used to
guarantee that a _____ product is produced.

2. Complete the following chart to show the reasons for using standard
components and for each give one advantage for the manufacturer.

	REASON	ADVANTAGE
A	Speeds up manufacture.	Reduces overheads.
B		
C		
D		
E		

3. In the box below fill in possible standard components that could
be used by a manufacturer when making the named product.

	STANDARD COMPONENTS			
Pizza				
Lasagne				
Chicken Curry				
Decorated Cake				
Strawberry Cheesecake				
Egg Mayonnaise sandwich				

4. There are also disadvantages of using standard components. Explain what these are.

1. Draw a star profile for the perfect cheese and onion crisps. Show at least 5 attributes.

2. Explain, in your own words, the importance of a taste evaluation chart.

3. Use the nutritional analysis chart for chicken pakoras on P.67 of your revision guide to answer the following questions.

(a) How many grams of protein are found in 100g of pakoras?

(b) Why might you decide to serve a green salad with the pakoras?

(c) How many kilocalories are there in one portion of pakoras?

(d) How could you use a nutritional analysis to help you develop a healthier product?

4. (a) A cake manufacturer has produced an ideal star profile for a lemon cake which they are developing. The team of technologists produces a prototype and they are at the stage of measuring their prototype against the ideal profile.

Plot the information below onto the ideal profile on the right, using a coloured pen.

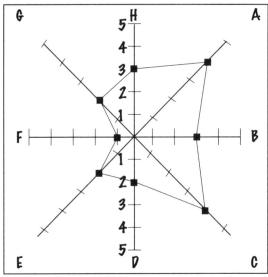

A) Lemon flavour (sponge)   1
B) Sweetness of overall cake   5
C) Depth of overall cake   2
D) Amount of lemon curd filling   5
E) Amount of icing on top   5
F) Yellow colour (sponge)   1
G) Stickiness of icing   3
H) Moist sponge   3

(b) Using the information from the two profiles suggest three areas which need to be improved and give details of how you would alter the prototype recipe.

(i) Area of improvement

Modification

(ii) Area of improvement

Modification

(iii) Area of improvement

Modification

5. Look at the label from some chocolate sponges and state how you could modify them to make a healthier product.

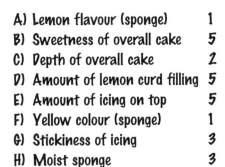

INGREDIENTS

Cream, Sugar, Water, Wheatflour, Egg, Sunflower Spread [contains Emulsifiers (Mono & Di-glycerides of Fatty Acids), Preservative (Potassium Sorbate), Natural Flavour, Citric Acid, Colour (Beta-Carotene)], Cocoa Powder (2%), Vegetable Suet, Syrup, Vegetable Oil, Modified Starch, Raising Agent (Sodium Bicarbonate). **Chocolate Sauce 26%.**

SUITABLE FOR VEGETARIANS

1. Name the following symbols and explain what they mean.

(i)	(ii)	(iii)	(iv)

2. Rearrange the following stages into the correct sequence for making small cakes. Draw the correct symbol around each letter. One has been done for you.

	START
A - Divide into bun cases	D
B - Cream margarine and sugar	
C - Are they cooked?	
D - Collect ingredients	
E - Sieve flour	
F - Beat egg	
G - Is egg beaten enough?	
H - Store	
I - Gradually add beaten egg	
J - Is mixture divided equally?	
K - Are margarine and sugar creamed enough?	
L - Cook in oven	
M - Package	
N - Cool	
O - Fold in flour	
P - Is all egg added?	
Q - Is the consistency correct?	
R - Is it cool enough to package?	
	END

1.   Define, in your own words, what makes a good quality food product.

2.   Write a definition of quality assurance.

3.   (a) List 3 different design-related areas which are covered by quality assurance.

(i)   (ii)   (iii)

(b) List 3 different manufacturing areas which are covered by quality assurance.

(i)   (ii)   (iii)

(c) List 3 different cost-related areas which are covered by quality assurance.

(i)   (ii)   (iii)

(d) List 3 other areas of quality assurance.

(i)   (ii)   (iii)

4.   Write a definition of quality control.

5.   Fill in the table below to show the quality control checks that a food manufacturer could have in place when making frozen sausage rolls.

During Designing	During Manufacture	At The End Of Manufacturing

1. **(a)** What does HACCP stand for?

(b) (i) What must food manufacturers do by law?

(ii) How do they do this?

2. **List and explain the three main types of hazard.**

(i)

(ii)

(iii)

3. **Complete the HACCP chart below.**

CCP or QC	PROCESS	HAZARD	RISK ASSESSMENT	CONTROL	TEST	REMEDIAL ACTION
CCP	Delivery of ingredients			Check containers	Visual	
		Chicken contains salmonella				Discard
CCP		Open containers		Check containers	Visual	
	Measure ingredients		High			Retrain workers
	Make curry sauce				Visual	Reduce amount of liquid
	Add chicken to sauce	Too little chicken			Visual	

4. Complete the following HACCP chart for the production of an egg mayonnaise sandwich.

CCP or QC	PROCESS	HAZARD	RISK ASSESSMENT	CONTROL	TEST	REMEDIAL ACTION
CCP	Delivery of ingredients	Dirty van	High	Check van Use reputable firm	Visual	Refuse delivery
CCP	Storage of ingredients	Incorrect storage - temperature (eggs, mayonnaise, butter) - Time (out of date, use by dates - all ingredients)	High / High	Check temperature of fridge (1-4°C) / Check all date stamps	Temperature Probe / Visual	Throw away / Throw away
	Hard boil eggs					
	Cool eggs					
QC	Shell eggs					
	Mix eggs with mayonnaise					
QC	Cut bread cakes					
	Butter bread cakes					
	Assemble sandwich					
	Package					
	Store					

1. One-off productions, such as special celebration cakes, are often more expensive than mass produced products. Why do you think this is?

2. Write definitions for the following, in your own words.

(i) Prototype -

(ii) One-off job -

(iii) Mass Production -

(iv) Batch Production -

(v) Continuous Flow Production -

(vi) Automated Manufacture -

(vii) CAM (include what the initials stand for) -

3. Which methods of production would be best for the following? (Give reasons for your answer).

(i) A wedding cake -

(ii) Jam tarts in a local bakery -

(iii) Ready-made pizzas -

(iv) Tins of spaghetti in tomato sauce -

(v) Bags of dried pasta -

1. Study the production line for small cakes illustrated below.
   List the checks that would take place at each of the circled numbers.

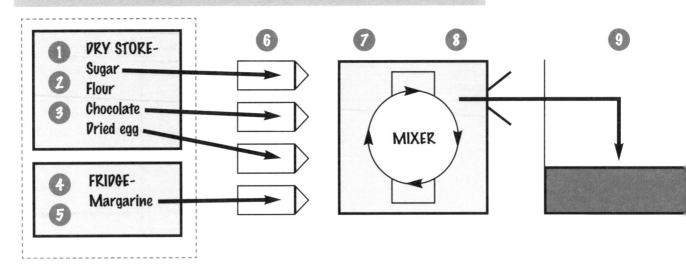

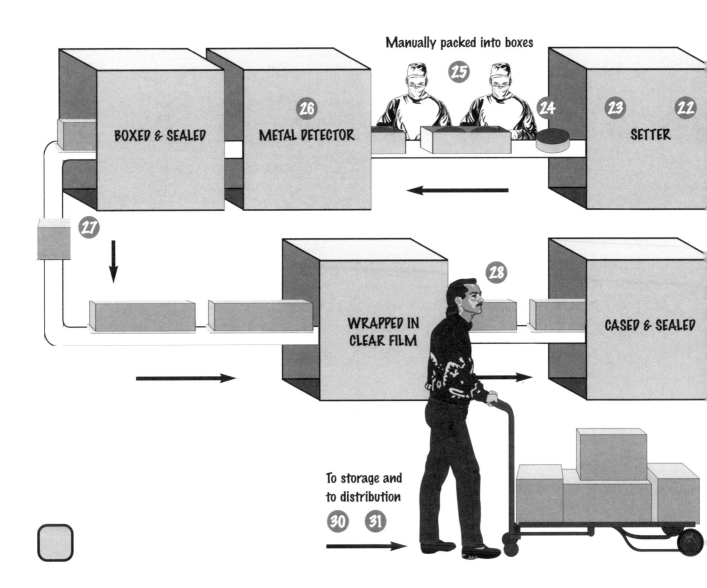

Manually packed into boxes

BOXED & SEALED

METAL DETECTOR

SETTER

WRAPPED IN CLEAR FILM

CASED & SEALED

To storage and to distribution

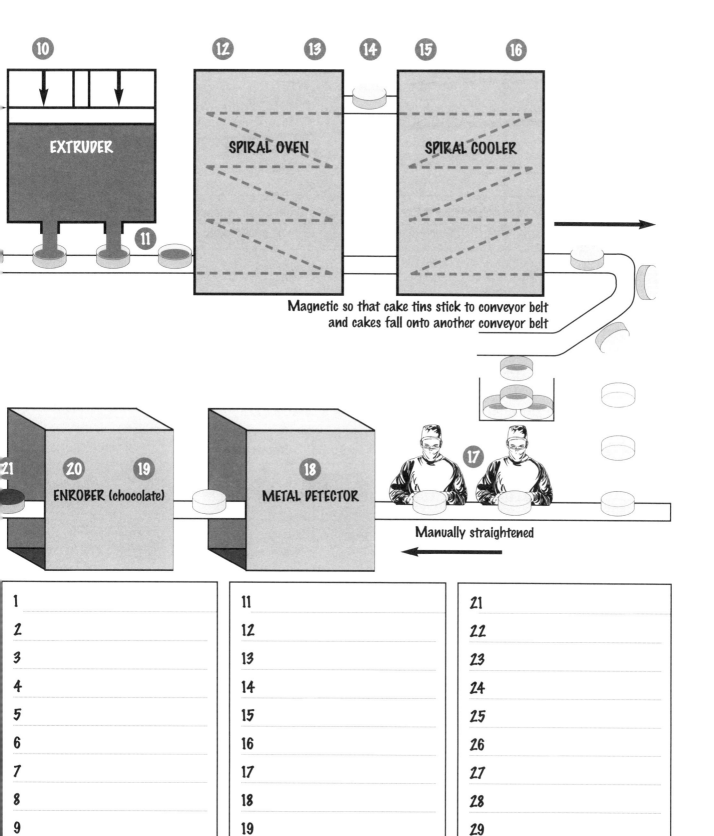

EXTRUDER

SPIRAL OVEN

SPIRAL COOLER

Magnetic so that cake tins stick to conveyor belt
and cakes fall onto another conveyor belt

ENROBER (chocolate)

METAL DETECTOR

Manually straightened

1	11	21
2	12	22
3	13	23
4	14	24
5	15	25
6	16	26
7	17	27
8	18	28
9	19	29
10	20	30
		31

1.   (a) Give six possible problems which might be encountered if a food was not packaged.

(b) A supermarket receives an order of baked beans from their supplier. They are packed in three layers of packaging. Give the collective name for each type of packaging.

Aluminium can -

A shallow paperboard box wrapped in plastic -

A pallet wrapped in plastic -

2.   For each of the following products state the packaging materials you would use and explain your reasons.

(a) A pizza bought in the frozen food section of a supermarket.

Material(s) used	Reasons used

(b) A jar of jam.

Material(s) used	Reasons used

(c) A pack of 6 chocolate coated biscuits.

Material(s) used	Reasons used

1. Explain why plastics are widely used in the food industry to package food.

2. (a) Why do you think thermoplastic packaging is the most common type used in the food industry?

(b) Name the four different types of thermoplastic packaging.

(i)

(ii)

(iii)

(iv)

3. Write the correct type of thermoplastic packaging next to each of the following characteristics.

CHARACTERISTIC	TYPE OF THERMOPLASTIC
Resistant to chemicals.	
Has a cushioning effect.	
Can be used as a film.	
Suitable for drinks.	
Rigid at high temperatures	
Has a high melting point.	
Resistant to acids.	

4. Explain the type of plastics used to package a cook-chill chicken korma.

5. Why do most food products use several types of packaging materials?

1. Explain why 'we use more packaging today than at any other time in history'.

2. (a) What types of packaging could be recycled? Explain which service(s) could be used.

(i) _____ (ii) _____ (iii) _____

(b) How can recycling sometimes be harmful to the environment?

3. Define the term 'biodegradable' and give an example of a product which uses this type of packaging.

4. Explain what the following symbols mean.

1. What information must be included on a food package by law?

2. Design a label for an instant dessert mix. Show what should be included by law as well as any other points you would add. Show the front and back of the package.

FRONT:

BACK:

3. A food manufacturer wants to add a food label to some jam.
What kind of label would he use? Explain your choice.

1. Below is a net for the packaging of a decorated chocolate cake. Fill in the boxes with relevant information/pictures etc.

NAME OF PRODUCT AND MANUFACTURER

WEIGHT

USE BY

MANUFACTURER

PRODUCT

GUARANTEE

PICTURE OF PRODUCT

STORAGE INSTRUCTIONS

MANUFACTURER'S NAME & ADDRESS

NUTRITIONAL INFORMATION

INGREDIENTS

2. Give 5 other pieces of information you could show on the packaging.

(i)

(ii)

(iii)

(iv)

(v)